ONE SPIRIT
BOOK OF DAYS

dbp

Welcome to the Year

Every new year is full of possibility, a chance to make a fresh start. As you consider your list of resolutions, how many relate to health, or self-discovery, or self-fulfilment?

We created the *One Spirit Book of Days* to be more than a journal. It's a resource for bringing balance to your life— with tools to help you keep your commitment to self-healing.

Every month starts off with a page of suggested goals for meditation, relaxation, energy, and detoxification. Think of them as guidelines for establishing a foundation of well-being on which to build throughout the year.

Each week, you'll find an inspiring quotation and a meditation to nurture mind, body and spirit. Accompanying each exercise is a colourful illustration. Whenever you glance at your journal, the artwork will be a visual reminder of the positive action you are taking toward your goals.

At the end of the diary are blank pages on which to record your progress—as well as dreams, hopes and insights that emerge as the year unfolds. Day by day, week by week, month by month, the *One Spirit Book of Days* will serve as a wise companion for all seasons of the spirit, all weathers of the heart.

January

The start of a new year is an auspicious time to set long-term goals. Pursuing a goal gives us a sense of purpose. But however motivated we are, the only worthwhile goals are those we have a chance of achieving. To succeed we must overcome fear of failure. Being too attached to a goal only increases the chance that we will fail. The paradox is that we must name our targets but also be prepared to let go of them. This allows us to be more spontaneous and relaxed.

Meditation goal

As you meditate, repeat the mantra "om" (pronounced in three syllables, ah-oh-mm) on each out-breath. The first syllable should vibrate in your abdomen, the second in your heart, the third behind your brow.

Relaxation goal

To help you sleep, visualize a rainbow-colored disk near your heart. Set it spinning until all the colors turn white. Hold the image of the spinning white disk in your mind as you drift off to sleep.

Energy goal

Eat plenty of fresh fruit and vegetables every day—they not only boost the immune system but offer us a living connection with the vital energy of the sun and the earth.

Detox goal

Begin to eliminate all stimulants to which you've become habituated, including coffee, tea, chocolate, alcohol, tobacco. If you're not ready to give up completely, cut down gradually—or set limits and stick to them.

January

Monday

Tuesday

Wednesday

"I frequently tramped eight or ten miles through the deepest snow to keep an appointment with a beech-tree, or a yellow birch, or an old acquaintance among the pines."
Henry David Thoreau (1817–1862)

The Lotus Blossom

In the rush of daily life, it is easy to get caught up in material concerns and neglect your spiritual side. To reconnect with your inner self, visualize a lotus blossom floating on a pond. Imagine light pouring outward through the petals, filling you with radiant calm, and restoring harmony to your life.

Thursday

Friday

Saturday

Sunday

January

Monday

_____
_____
_____
_____
_____
_____
_____
_____
_____
_____
_____
_____

Tuesday

_____
_____
_____
_____
_____
_____
_____
_____
_____
_____
_____
_____

Wednesday

_____
_____
_____
_____
_____
_____
_____
_____
_____
_____
_____
_____

"Whoever holds in their mind the great image of oneness, the world will come to them. It will flow and not be obstructed—coming in safety, oneness, and peace."
Tao Te Ching (4th century BCE)

THE LAW OF ATTRACTION

*To make yourself a magnet for what you deeply desire, you will
need to stay alert to opportunities that present themselves. A
desire and its fulfillment are drawn together in a mystical way.
Watch for signs and be ready to act on them.*

Thursday

Friday

Saturday

Sunday

January

Monday

Tuesday

Wednesday

"I believe that unarmed truth and unconditional love will have the final word in reality."

Martin Luther King, Jr. (1929–1968)

THE PALMIST'S KISS

Imagine you are filled with fast-flowing energy. Then, share a "palmist's kiss" with someone. Sit facing one another. Raise your hands and press your left palm to your partner's right palm, your right palm to his left. Close your eyes and visualize energy flowing between you in a continuous two-way exchange, cleansing you both of all fear.

Thursday

_____
_____
_____
_____
_____
_____
_____
_____
_____
_____
_____
_____

Friday

_____
_____
_____
_____
_____
_____
_____
_____
_____
_____
_____
_____

Saturday

_____
_____
_____
_____
_____
_____

Sunday

_____
_____
_____
_____
_____
_____

January

Monday

Tuesday

Wednesday

"The eye by which I see God is the same eye by which God sees me."
Meister Eckhart (1260–1327)

THROUGH THE EYES OF A CAT

Looking at life through another's eyes gives us a fresh perspective. Spend five minutes imagining you are a cat. Curl up in a ball on some cushions on the floor. Close your eyes and breathe deeply. Listen carefully to every sound. Now, open your eyes and look around you. See if you can bring that same alert awareness to everything you do.

Thursday

_____
_____
_____
_____
_____
_____
_____
_____
_____
_____
_____
_____

Friday

_____
_____
_____
_____
_____
_____
_____
_____
_____
_____
_____
_____

Saturday

_____
_____
_____
_____
_____

Sunday

_____
_____
_____
_____
_____

January

Monday	Tuesday	Wednesday

"Sleep is as powerful as a sultan."

Egyptian proverb

Sleep's Antechamber

After a stressful day, it can be difficult to relax yourself ready for sleep. Once in bed, imagine yourself walking down a flight of steps, feeling increasingly tired as you descend, before entering a beautiful bedroom. You watch yourself lie down on the sumptuous bed and sink into the soft covers. Tell yourself, "I am falling into a deep peaceful sleep," as you drift off.

Thursday

_____
_____
_____
_____
_____
_____
_____
_____
_____
_____
_____
_____
_____

Friday

_____
_____
_____
_____
_____
_____
_____
_____
_____
_____
_____
_____
_____

Saturday

_____
_____
_____
_____
_____

Sunday

_____
_____
_____
_____
_____
_____
_____

February

One question we all face as spiritual beings is how much worldly pleasure to give up. Traditionally, a monk turns his back on material comforts to devote himself to good works and the health of his soul. For the rest of us, denial of at least some earthly desires offers us a freedom from attachment that leads to joy. We do not have to become monks. But if we stop overconsuming, we can live with the satisfaction of knowing that we are not depleting the earth's precious resources.

Meditation goal

Practice loving kindness. Start by wishing happiness and health for people you know well and for mere acquaintances. Then extend such wishes to people you do not like. Find love in your heart for your enemies.

Relaxation goal

In stressful situations, such as a job interview or a difficult discussion, visualize a friend looking over your shoulder, cheering you on with good wishes. Take heart from the faith your friend shows in you.

Energy goal

Sleep is nature's best restorative. To develop good sleep habits, stay away from stimulants, listen to gentle music before you retire, and try not to rehash the day's problems as you lie in bed.

Detox goal

Plan strategies to eliminate stress. To relieve symptoms—nervous tension, insomnia, headaches, mild depression—ask your partner or a friend to give you a massage with lavender oil.

February

Monday

Tuesday

Wednesday

"When breathing in a long breath [the meditator] knows that he breathes in a long breath, when breathing in a short breath he knows that he breathes in a short breath."

Anapanasati Sutra (*c.*300–100 BCE)

The Isle of Calm

When we are anxious, our breathing becomes shallow and rapid. To calm yourself, imagine that you are lying on a beach on a tropical island. You can hear waves gently lapping against the shore. Listen to your in-breaths and out-breaths, then try to synchronize them with the sound of the waves. As your breathing slows and deepens, you will automatically relax.

Thursday

Friday

Saturday

Sunday

February

Monday

Tuesday

Wednesday

"Do not seek to follow in the footsteps of the ancient ones; seek what they sought."
Bassho (1644–1694)

STEPPING STONES TO PEACE

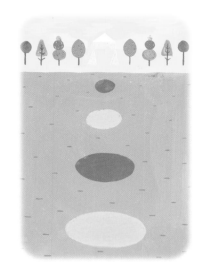

Even far-off goals are attainable if we lay out a realistic path toward them and try each day to work toward reaching another stepping stone. But do not feel disappointed if, on any one day, you make only half your intended progress, or even no progress at all. The mere act of thinking about your goals will bring you closer to them.

Thursday

_____
_____
_____
_____
_____
_____
_____
_____
_____
_____
_____
_____

Friday

_____
_____
_____
_____
_____
_____
_____
_____
_____
_____
_____
_____

Saturday

_____
_____
_____
_____
_____

Sunday

_____
_____
_____
_____
_____
_____

February

Monday

Tuesday

Wednesday

"The sun alone explains the sun; love alone can explain love."
Rumi (1207–1273)

SHIATSU FOR STRESS

"Connection shiatsu" can relieve short, shallow breathing caused by stress. Lie on your back and place the palm of one hand on your abdomen, the palm of the other on your chest. Hold for one minute. This will stimulate the flow of chi between your lungs and your kidneys (the "seat" of anxiety), helping you to relax and breathe more deeply.

Thursday

Friday

Saturday

Sunday

February

Monday	Tuesday	Wednesday

"The soul who meditates on the Self is content to serve the Self and remains satisfied within the Self—there is nothing further to achieve."

Bhagavad Gita (c.200 BCE)

The Sleep Experiment

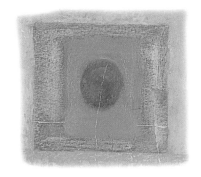

Go to bed when tired but not exhausted. Note the time. Listen to gentle music, read a soothing book, or meditate just before sleep. Don't set your alarm; allow yourself to wake naturally. How long did you sleep? Repeat this exercise every night until your sleep pattern becomes regular. This is your natural and most restful sleep cycle.

Thursday

Friday

Saturday

Sunday

February

Monday

Tuesday

Wednesday

"Our cup is the moon; our wine is the sun."
Ibn al-Farid (1181–1235)

NATURE'S GIFTS

Fruit symbolizes nature's abundance. Place some fruits on a table and, after closing your eyes and turning your awareness inward, call them up in your mind. Imagine them ripening, in some faraway land—note their shape and texture, their gradations of hue, their intricate patterning. Here, even in February, are the gifts of the natural world, in miniature.

Thursday

_____

Friday

_____

Saturday

_____

Sunday

_____

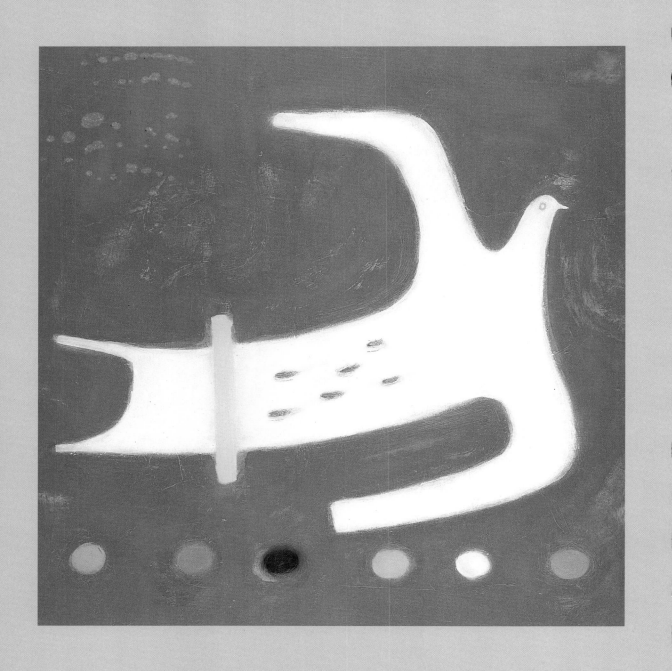

March

When we set out to change, we become the heroes of our own spiritual quest. And, like the great heroes of myth, we must slay the demons of illusion (low self-esteem, laziness, attachment to habit) with the sword of knowledge and the shield of courage. It may help to dramatize your resolve in these terms. Devise a program for change, then pour your energies into carrying out the project. This is how inner dragons are brought low.

Meditation goal

As a Zen master said, the sky does not impede the clouds in their flight. Meditate on this notion. See it as an image of the mind in meditation: let your thoughts, like clouds, drift in and out, without trying to stop them.

Relaxation goal

Let go of attachment to lost opportunities—the things you couldn't do because you were doing something else instead. Embrace your chosen course of action, and you'll forget about the road left unexplored.

Energy goal

Instead of taking the elevator, make a habit of walking up the stairs—or at least the last few floors. You can even treat this as a meditative exercise, and silently repeat a mantra as you climb.

Detox goal

Eat fresh food whenever you can, and cut down on processed foods. By doing this, you give your body more vital nutrients and decrease your intake of unhealthy additives, as well as fat and sugar.

March

Monday

Tuesday

Wednesday

"Anyone who is truly kind can never be unhappy. Anyone who is truly wise can never be muddled."

Confucius (551–479 BCE)

THE TREE OF LIFE

We are no more defined by our physical appearance than a tree is defined by its trunk. Similarly, our experiences, like the branches of a tree, might seem to shape us, but they do not. Meditate on your inner self—the core of your being that cannot be battered by circumstances. This is the essence of who you really are.

Thursday

Friday 1

Saturday 2

Sunday 3

March

Monday 4

Tuesday 5

Wednesday 6

"All the way to heaven is heaven."
St. Catherine of Siena (1347–1380)

THE UNBIDDEN ANSWER

"Who am I?" is an endlessly fascinating question. As you watch your mind in meditation, you will notice moments of space in between thoughts when the mind is apparently free of content. Yet something remains. What might this be? Do not pursue this question, simply ask it. One day the answer will arise of its own accord, from the depths of your intuitive wisdom.

Thursday 28

Friday 29

Saturday 30

Sunday 31

GALLOPING EMOTIONS

Sometimes emotions behave like wild horses, straining to break free of our control. When this happens, try to step back for a moment and remain calm. Bear in mind that your horses can respond to will, intelligence, and reason. If you mentally ask them to stay in their stalls, they will do so. It is only with your permission that they can break free.

Thursday

Friday

Saturday

Sunday

May

We fear spontaneity because it seems unreliable—when we take a plunge, we have no idea where we will end up. However, by breaking out of our comfort zone, we can experience life more fully, and thereby learn and grow. Every moment is a chance to take our habitual patterns of thought and behavior and splash them with flamboyant color. Each minute of habit is a minute of spiritual inertia; each minute of freedom is a minute of vibrant wakefulness.

Meditation goal

Meditate on flowers. Composite flowers, such as gerberas, that are beautifully symmetrical make perfect mandalas. Fill your mind with the pure experience of their color and geometry.

Relaxation goal

Learn to identify the true voice of your conscience, and avoid confusing it with social pressure. You will know deep down if you are on the right course—it may not be the course that others want you to follow.

Energy goal

Use polarity to increase energy. Lower your body into a squat with feet slightly apart. Shift your weight in a circular motion, then rock gently to and fro. This releases tension in the pelvis, allowing energy to flow.

Detox goal

Make a point of taking time over meals, and relax for a while afterwards, if you can. Drink water or juice before, not with or after, meals: it can reduce absorption of nutrients and upset digestion.

May

Monday

Tuesday

Wednesday 01

"In order to find Perfect Wisdom, one must go through the door of one's self-nature."
Chinese proverb (7th century CE)

DRAWING THE FACE

Most of us find it hard to close our eyes and create a vivid mental picture of our own face. If you run your fingers over your face, you can sharpen this mental image and give yourself a facial massage at the same time. Once the image is crystal-clear in your mind, the massage is complete.

Thursday 16

Friday 17

Saturday 18

Sunday 19

May

Monday 20

Tuesday 21

Wednesday 22

*"The quiet, solitary person apprehends the inscrutable—seeking nothing, holding to
the middle way, and remaining free from attachments."*
I Ching (c.300 BCE)

PATTERNS OF LIVING

Look at the design of your life. Does every day hold moments of special significance, such as keeping a promise to yourself or to another? Give priority to what fulfills you. Wake up to your real needs, and create a new life design around them. Keep the design flexible, so you can readily adapt it to changing circumstances and interests.

Thursday 23

Friday 24

Saturday 25

Sunday 26

May

Monday 27

Tuesday 28

Wednesday 29

"The mind is everything; what you think, you become."
The Buddha (*c.*563–483 BCE)

THE ZEN GARDEN

A Zen garden is one that captures the beauty of natural scenery while maintaining an emphasis on simplicity. You can make your own miniature Zen garden in a sand pit: carefully rake the sand around larger stones and meditate on the beautiful patterns you create. Acknowledge that truth can be discovered all around us, even in the sand and stones beneath our feet.

Thursday 30

Friday 31

Saturday

Sunday

June

People who are not fully awake to themselves tend to build walls that separate them from others—like hibernating animals holed up in their protective dens. But what happens when we reach beyond the barrier and make a connection—with a new neighbor, perhaps, or someone we meet on vacation? Through the sharing of spirit, we discover our links with all humanity. Use some of your summer leisure time to reach out to strangers with openness and love.

Meditation goal

At the summer solstice, do a meditation on the life-giving powers of the sun. Sit facing the brightest part of the horizon, close your eyes, and bask in the glow of light filtered through your eyelids.

Relaxation goal

Fine-tune your relationship with yourself. This is just as important for inner peace as your relationships with others. Start to accept what you cannot change—and start to change what you cannot accept.

Energy goal

Make time in your life for laughter, which is an instant energizer. Laughter stimulates the solar plexus and sacral chakras. (So does crying, which also should be released if the need arises.)

Detox goal

Start the day with an energy-giving fruit breakfast, such as guava, banana, peach, and grapes, chopped and mixed with unsweetened fruit juice, coconut (freshly grated if possible), and wheatgerm flakes.

June

Monday

Tuesday

Wednesday

"It is necessary to know only that love is a direction, rather than a state of the soul."
Simone Weil (1909–1943)

GIVE AND TAKE

When life's demands seem overwhelming and we are giving constantly to others, it is easy to neglect ourselves. Imagine yourself as a pitcher pouring out your love to all around you, then giving yourself an emotional refill. Take a few minutes each day to nurture yourself. The key to true happiness is a balance of give and take.

Thursday

Friday

Saturday 01

Sunday 02

June

Monday 3

Tuesday 4

Wednesday 5

"Speech is the second of our possessions, after the spirit. Perhaps, indeed, we have no other possessions in the world."
Gabriela Mistral (1889–1957)

THE SALMON

Before we let logic overrule our intuition, we should meditate on the symbolism of the leaping salmon: time and again instinct guides it back to its spawning ground upriver, ensuring the survival of the species. We, too, need to trust instinct to guide us. Like the salmon's, our survival depends on it.

Thursday 6

Friday 7

Saturday 8

Sunday 9

June

Monday 10

Tuesday 11

Wednesday 12

"The thirsty look for water. But water also looks for the thirsty."
Rumi (1207–1273)

THE WISHING WELL

It is important for all of us, male and female alike, to stay in touch with our nurturing side. Imagine that you are drinking water from a well—a traditionally feminine symbol. The sweet, clear water—the essence of life—refreshes and relaxes you. Now make a wish. In your mind's eye, toss the wish into the well, and give thanks to Mother Earth for her bounty.

Thursday   13

Friday   14

Saturday   15

Sunday   16

June

Monday 17

Tuesday 18

Wednesday 19

"Not to be gladdened by praise, nor to be upset by blame, but to know completely one's own virtues or powers—these are the qualities of excellence."

Saskya Pandita (1182–1251)

Zen Flowers

Create a Zen flower arrangement, symbolically reflecting the three realms of the universe: Heaven, Earth and the human world. As you build your composition, focus on each element you add, and be aware also of the dancing movements of your hands. Once the task is complete, feel a connection between yourself and the arrangement: meditate on the flowers in all their singular beauty.

Thursday 27

Friday 28

Saturday 29

Sunday 30.

ENDLESS ENERGY

Think of the sun, endlessly pouring energy onto our world. Our own spirits are similarly inexhaustible. As channels for universal energy, we can pour out love, without our reserves ever running dry. Meditate on your role as an endless source of love, to be given freely to everyone you encounter.

Thursday 11

Friday 12

Saturday 13

Sunday 14.

July

Monday 15

Tuesday 16

Wednesday 17

"The milk of cows of any color is white. The sages declare that the milk is wisdom, and that the cows are the sacred scriptures."

Amritabindu Upanishad (*c.*600 BCE)

THE POMEGRANATE

We sometimes forget that other people are different from ourselves and are entitled to their principles and opinions. Think of all those viewpoints as the countless seeds in a pomegranate fruit—many tiny parts that together make up a whole, reflecting the rich diversity of all creation. Criticism generates discord, but tolerance and compassion encourage peace and harmony.

Thursday 18

Friday 19

Saturday 20

Sunday 21

July

Monday 22

Tuesday 23

Wednesday 24

"If you really know how to live, what better way to start the day than with a smile?"
Thich Nhat Hanh (b.1926)

SEA TUMBLING

A good relaxation exercise is to immerse yourself in the vastness of an imaginary sea and let its power cleanse you of anxiety. This exercise works well for those who find visualization difficult: all you need to do is conjure the feeling of the sea and its turbulent energy. As an ancient Tibetan Buddhist text tells us, the aim is "to swim within the energies of the senses."

Thursday 25

Friday 26

Saturday 27

Sunday 28

July

Monday 29

Tuesday 30

Wednesday 31

"The heart that feels things deeply has wisdom. And wisdom as profound as that gives rise to virtue."

Chuang-tzu (*c.*350 BCE)

ALONG THE GRAIN OF NATURE

We can learn much from the Taoist principle of wu wei: *action through inaction. Essential to wu wei is not to exert pointless effort or to go against nature: both are thought to lead to the opposite of the desired result. Strength sometimes comes more from doing nothing—and allowing matters to resolve themselves.*

Thursday

Friday

Saturday

Sunday

August

Mumonkan—the "gateless gate"—is a collection of Zen sayings that at first seem nonsensical but point to profound truth. The gate is at once a "thing" (a mental barrier to pass through) and a "no-thing" (an illusion that keeps us from realizing our true nature). Through meditation we see that what comes between us and the ability to find peace is the constant internal chatter of our minds. Meditation takes us beyond this chatter to the essential calm within.

Meditation goal

While meditating, imagine your breath flowing into your body in the form of white light. Then imagine it exiting in the form of gray or black smoke that contains all your tension and exhaustion.

Relaxation goal

Refuse to put up with stress. If meditation or yoga fails to reduce your stress level, set aside a day to diagnose the causes. Eliminate whatever external stressors you can, then draft a new program of self-care.

Energy goal

Learn the basic Chi Kung position—a relaxed standing posture, with arms hanging at your sides. Imagine you are a tree: with each in-breath, draw energy from the earth; with each out-breath, expel anxieties.

Detox goal

Use a generous amount of garlic daily—a clove a day, taken raw or cooked in a meal, or as a capsule or tincture. Garlic cleanses the blood, lowers blood cholesterol levels, and works as a natural antibiotic.

August

Monday	Tuesday	Wednesday

"As bees sip nectar from many flowers and make a hive of honey, so that not one drop can claim, 'I am from this flower or that,' all creatures, though one, do not realize they are one."

Chandogya Upanishad (c.800–700 BCE)

The Beehive

Worries often buzz around in our heads like bees around a hive, creating a perpetual background hum of anxiety. To help retune your mind, imagine a hive surrounded by honeybees, with each bee representing a niggling problem. Now visualize the bees disappearing one at a time into the hive, and notice how the buzz in your mind quiets down.

Thursday 01

Friday 02

Saturday 03

Sunday 04

August

Monday 05

Tuesday 06

Wednesday 07

"There is no real coming and going, for what is going if not coming?"
Sa'di of Shiraz (c.1213–91)

RELEASING SADNESS

Whenever you feel sad, take yourself for a walk. Focus your attention on whatever you see as you pass. It doesn't matter where you go or how often you follow the same path. With each step, you dislodge negative feelings and open yourself positively to sights, sounds, and smells.

Thursday 08

Friday 09

Saturday 10

Sunday 11

August

Monday 12

Tuesday 13

Wednesday 14

"I try to teach my heart to want nothing it can't have."
Alice Walker (b.1944)

SEA SHELLS

The shell is a symbol of good fortune for Chinese Buddhists. We may feel that we are disadvantaged compared to others, but we all experience instances of good fortune—our own collection of shells. Think of your friendships, your travel experiences, your reading. Good fortune lies all around; you need only to gather the blessings you find on your path.

Thursday 15

Friday 16

Saturday 17

Sunday 18

August

Monday 19

Tuesday 20

Wednesday 21

"Why do you want to open the outside door when there is an inside door?"
Yogaswami (1872–1964)

THE SRI YANTRA

The sri yantra *is a Tantric symbol for the creation of the universe. This image can speak directly to the unconscious mind, producing an experience of profound harmony and mystical oneness with the forces represented by the geometry of the figure. As you meditate on the yantra, sense the design both in front of you and inside your mind.*

Thursday 22

Friday 23

Saturday 24

Sunday 25

August

Monday 26

Tuesday 27

Wednesday 28

"All of existence is imagination within imagination, while God alone is true Being."
Ibn al-'Arabi (1165–1240)

MINDFUL BREATH

Often, it is when we are simply sitting and paying attention to our breath that our true nature reveals itself. While meditating, focus on the passage of air as you breathe in and out through your nostrils. If your thoughts wander, bring them gently back to focus on your breathing. With practice, your mind will come increasingly under control.

Thursday 29

Friday 30

Saturday 31

Sunday

September

The enlightened mind feels no sorrow at the passing of summer and the first bite of cold air announcing fall. As the nights get longer, so does the time for undistracted thought and for the quiet virtues of a lamplit interior. Relish the last vestiges of summer warmth and evening light, but do not cling to them. All phases of nature's cycle are equal in their goodness. True spiritual awareness means giving thanks as the wheel turns: it does not indulge in regret.

Meditation goal

Focus on the sounds and shapes of your environment. Recognize the extent to which the world flows through you and you flow through it. Feeling a kinship with all creation leads to gratitude.

Relaxation goal

Picture your past as a museum set in a beautiful landscape. You may visit it now and then, but you can easily walk away from it. You know that it is still there, but you have more exciting places to discover.

Energy goal

Practice breathing properly, in a relaxed way, using the diaphragm. As you inhale, your abdomen rises; exhale, and it lowers. Diaphragm breathing improves ventilation in the lungs, with minimum energy expenditure.

Detox goal

Enjoy the bounty of fall: apples, pears, squash. Fresh fruits and vegetables contain insoluble fiber, which speeds the elimination of wastes and helps protect against cancer, heart disease, and bowel problems.

September

Monday

Tuesday

Wednesday

"You are alone with everything you love."
Novalis (1771–1801)

GARDEN MEDITATION

Pick a handful of leaves from the different trees or shrubs in your garden, or in a nearby park. Sit comfortably and study the leaves—their shapes, colors, and textures. Feel their textures by pressing them into your palms. Trace the vein in each leaf with your finger. Meditate on the patterns and hues you see.

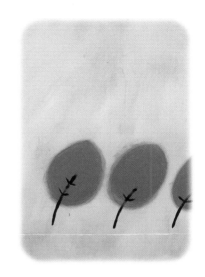

Thursday

Friday

Saturday

Sunday 01

September

Monday 02

Tuesday 03

Wednesday 04

"The mind is everything. What we think, we become."
The Buddha (*c.*563–483 BCE)

THE WHEEL OF LAW

The Hindu symbol of the chakravartin—*the wheel of law—symbolizes unobstructed movement and completeness. Think of the wheel as a representation of yourself: the hub is your true, perfect nature; the spokes are aspects of your personality; the outer rim is your worldly form. Concentrate on how the hub holds the wheel together. Then meditate on the point at the very center—the divine spirit at the heart of us all.*

Thursday 05

Friday 06

Saturday 07

Sunday 08

September

Monday 09

Tuesday 10

Wednesday 11

"Keep your face to the sunshine and you cannot see the shadows."
Helen Keller (1880–1968)

The Setting Sun

Life's fleeting moments are often accompanied by sadness. To help you regard the passing of time in a positive way, meditate on the cycle of the sun. Its pure light rises and traverses the heavens until it reaches full strength, then gradually grows richer in tone as it sets in a spectacular array of color. Why feel sorrow for a natural process?

Thursday 12

Friday 13

Saturday 14

Sunday 15.

September

Monday 16   Tuesday 17   Wednesday 18

"All things in this world are created out of God's love, and they become a framework of gifts, offered to us so that we can know God more easily and make a return of love more readily."

St. Ignatius Loyola (1491–1556)

THE INTUITIVE WAY

When a flock of birds flies in perfect formation, we are amazed at their instinctive ability to synchronize. An interesting exercise is to list your own innate skills: the ability to love, for instance, or to feel empathy. These are gifts of the spirit, available in some measure to us all. In listing them, we acknowledge our spiritual inventory.

Thursday 26

Friday 27

Saturday 28

Sunday 29

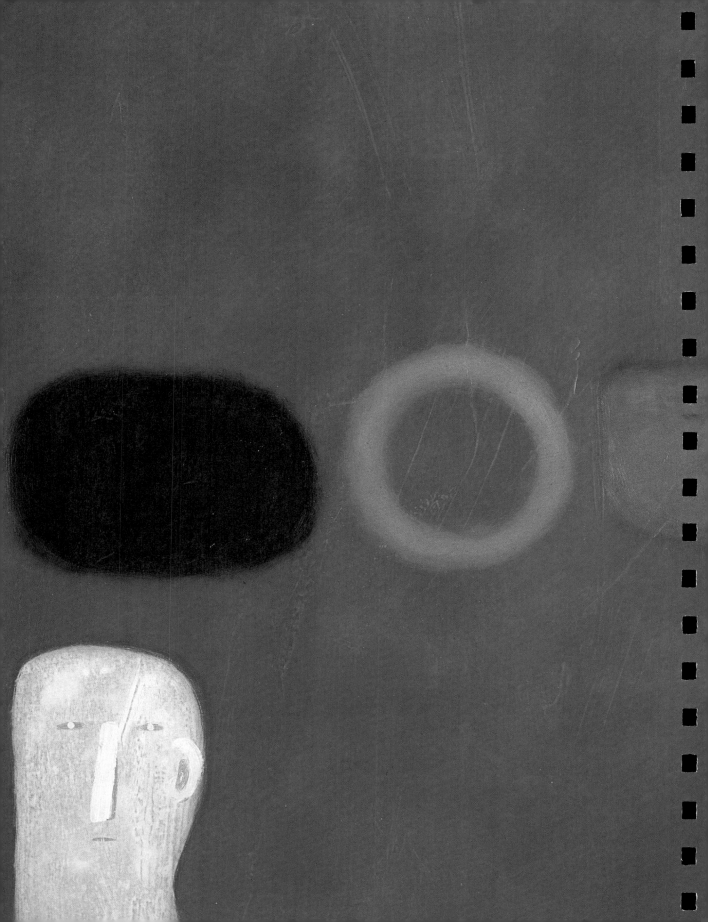

October

The senses are windows through which energy flows in both directions. Our eyes receive visual messages and they also show how we feel. Our ears take in the sounds of life, while in "lending an ear" we give comfort. We use our mouths to taste flavors, and also to tell a joke or offer counsel. Touch, as well as letting us feel temperature and texture, transmits love and reassurance. Our senses are more than instruments of perception: they are deep-rooted aspects of the self.

Meditation goal

Do a peace meditation once a week. Focus on resolving discord, by imagining harmony radiating out from your intentions. As you repeat this, you will make peace a reality, turning a wish into a feeling.

Relaxation goal

Spend a day on retreat—in the privacy of your own home. Make arrangements with your family to avoid disturbance, and devote the day to quiet contemplation or soothing physical work in the house or garden.

Energy goal

Make dancing a part of your life. It is energizing and aerobic—and a joyful way to release tension. You do not have to go to a club or give a party—you can turn on some music and cut loose at home.

Detox goal

Experiment with making juices, and keep notes on your favorite combinations. Apple, grapes, oranges, and carrots all make cleansing tonics. Buy organic; if you can't, be sure to peel fruits and vegetables.

October

Monday

Tuesday 01

Wednesday 02

"Love is an image of God—not a lifeless image, but the living essence of the all-divine nature which shines full of goodness."

Martin Luther (1483–1546)

A BALL OF ENERGY

Central to Indian philosophy is prana, *the life-force we inhale with the breath. The Chinese call it* chi. *To feel its energy, stand with legs apart and place your hands in front of your lower abdomen, palms facing each other. Imagine your hands encircling a ball of energy emanating from below your navel. Your fingers may tingle, or your hands might feel warm.*

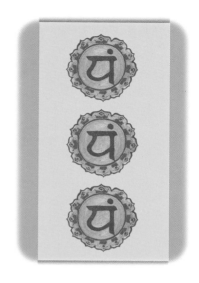

Thursday 03

Friday 04

Saturday 05

Sunday 06

October

Monday 07

Tuesday 08

Wednesday 09

"The mind must be kept independent of any thoughts that blossom within it. If the mind becomes dependent upon anything, it has no safe haven."

The Diamond Sutra (c.200–300 CE)

The Fruits of Awareness

On a country walk or a stroll in the park, rather than experiencing nature as a backdrop to your thoughts, put your personal preoccupations on hold, and give your undivided attention to each living thing you see. As you do, a sense of deep connection will gradually ripen at the core of your being.

Thursday
_____
_____
_____
_____
_____
_____
_____
_____
_____
_____
_____
_____
_____

Friday
_____
_____
_____
_____
_____
_____
_____
_____
_____
_____
_____
_____
_____

Saturday
_____
_____
_____
_____
_____
_____
_____

Sunday
_____
_____
_____
_____
_____
_____

October

Monday

Tuesday

Wednesday

"The real voyage of discovery consists not in seeking new landscapes but in having new eyes."

Marcel Proust (1871–1922)

THE CYCLE OF LIFE

The truest response we can make to changes in the weather and the seasons is one of acceptance—indeed of joy. As autumn approaches, welcome nature's turning—it shows us the life-sustaining impermanence of all things, and mirrors the cycle of human existence from birth to death and rebirth. Joy in life is joy in change.

Thursday

_____

_____

_____

_____

_____

_____

_____

_____

_____

_____

_____

Friday

_____

_____

_____

_____

_____

_____

_____

_____

_____

_____

_____

Saturday

_____

_____

_____

_____

_____

Sunday

_____

_____

_____

_____

_____

_____

November

When we are children, our imaginations are at their most fertile. As we grow older, we become preoccupied with "real" life, forgetting that our fanciful creations can give great pleasure. If we use the imagination at all, it is often as the servant of pessimism: What would happen if I lost my job? What if my husband left me tomorrow? Creative visualization is, by definition, positive. Setting aside disaster scenarios, we can summon up images that enable us to approach our problems constructively.

Meditation goal

Visualize a point of consciousness behind your forehead and imagine it transmitting energy into the world. End your meditation with the thought that, as long as you live, this outpouring will never cease.

Relaxation goal

Appreciate to the fullest the satisfaction of loving and giving. It is hard to be truly happy if those closest to us are not. Our own goodness is reflected back to us in the happiness of family and friends.

Energy goal

Travel provides a great opportunity for relaxation and exercise. Avoid crowds by going at off-peak hours. Take steps to ensure your comfort; walk or cycle when you can. Stressful travel drains your energy.

Detox goal

Try to cut down the time you spend in front of a computer terminal each day and be sure to take frequent breaks. Also, use a standard telephone, not a cellular, whenever you have a choice.

November

Monday

Tuesday

Wednesday

"Be gentle toward everyone, but stern with yourself."
St. Teresa of Ávila (1515–1582)

GOODNESS AND KARMA

Imagine that all your actions are like drops of rain falling on a pond. The ripples they make represent the signals you send out to the people around you. When the waves hit the bank, they turn and come back toward you. In the same way, if you send out goodness, you can expect goodness in return. That is the law of karma.

Thursday

_____
_____
_____
_____
_____
_____
_____
_____
_____
_____
_____
_____
_____

Friday

_____
_____
_____
_____
_____
_____
_____
_____
_____
_____
_____
_____
_____

Saturday

_____
_____
_____
_____

Sunday

_____
_____
_____
_____
_____
_____
_____

November

Monday

Tuesday

Wednesday

"An optimist is a person who sees a green light everywhere, while the pessimist sees only a red stoplight. The truly wise person is color-blind."

Albert Schweitzer (1875–1965)

THE RAINBOW

In times of difficulty, look to the heavens to lift your spirits. Picture a rainbow and ponder how something so beautiful could emerge from a dark and violent storm. Meditate on each of the rainbow's colors, then let the spectrum dissolve into a beam of pure white light. Reflect on the oneness this signifies, and feel the healing power of spiritual harmony filling you with peace.

Thursday

_____
_____
_____
_____
_____
_____
_____
_____
_____
_____
_____
_____
_____
_____

Friday

_____
_____
_____
_____
_____
_____
_____
_____
_____
_____
_____
_____
_____

Saturday

_____
_____
_____
_____
_____

Sunday

_____
_____
_____
_____
_____

November

Monday

Tuesday

Wednesday

"Those of us who know the truth are not equal to those of us who love the truth."
Confucius (551–479 BCE)

A Voyage to the Center of the Self

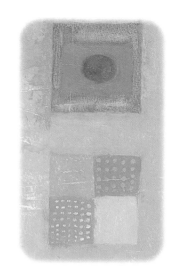

Imagine you are floating in a warm ocean. On the sea bed you spot the wreck of a galleon. You swim down and enter the ship through an opening in the hull. The farther in you go, the brighter the water becomes. At the center lies a chest of precious objects: each one is an aspect of your true self. Swim back to the surface, relaxed in the knowledge of your worth.

Thursday

_____
_____
_____
_____
_____
_____
_____
_____
_____
_____
_____
_____

Friday

_____
_____
_____
_____
_____
_____
_____
_____
_____
_____
_____
_____

Saturday

_____
_____
_____
_____
_____
_____

Sunday

_____
_____
_____
_____
_____
_____

November

Monday	Tuesday	Wednesday

"Once I have determined to move toward enlightenment, even though at times I might become fatigued or distracted, streams of merit pour down from the heavens."

Shantideva (*c.*700 CE)

A WINDOW TO THE FUTURE

Often we dwell on the past because we are fearful of the future, but in order to grow we have to overcome our fear. Imagine the future as a peaceful stretch of countryside. Imagine yourself looking at it through a window. Open the window and welcome the gentle winds of change. When you see that there is nothing to fear, you can embrace the future with confidence.

Thursday

_____
_____
_____
_____
_____
_____
_____
_____
_____
_____
_____
_____
_____

Friday

_____
_____
_____
_____
_____
_____
_____
_____
_____
_____
_____
_____
_____

Saturday

_____
_____
_____
_____
_____
_____

Sunday

_____
_____
_____
_____
_____
_____

November

Monday

Tuesday

Wednesday

"Heaven does not cause winter to cease, just because we do not like the cold."
Chinese proverb

THE WIZARD

The wizard symbolizes the wisdom that comes with age. Imagine yourself gaining power as the years settle on your head like snow. Visualize snowflakes falling slowly, adding to your store of insights. Reflect on the vast knowledge that humankind has accumulated since the first flake fell on earth.

Thursday

_____
_____
_____
_____
_____
_____
_____
_____
_____
_____
_____
_____
_____

Friday

_____
_____
_____
_____
_____
_____
_____
_____
_____
_____
_____
_____
_____

Saturday

_____
_____
_____
_____
_____
_____

Sunday

_____
_____
_____
_____
_____
_____

December

Our life purpose is what we live by. Identifying your mission and setting out on the journey to fulfill it can in itself bring contentment. If we know where we are going, we can afford to relax from time to time—indeed, letting go of our goals is, paradoxically, an important step toward achieving them. Allow your purpose to unfold and flower. You will want to act on opportunities as they arise, but the energy of the universe will be on your side.

Meditation goal

Try meditation to ease minor aches and pains. On each in-breath, imagine white light flooding the body, then, on each out-breath, imagine it flowing to the place where the pain is most acute.

Relaxation goal

Observe the winter solstice with a ceremonial meal for family or friends. You can make positive plans together for the following year, and take the first step to put into effect at least one of those plans.

Energy goal

To improve the quality of your sleep, listen to natural sounds just before you go to bed—a CD of birdsong perhaps, or waves breaking. You could even record your own tape with sounds from a place you love.

Detox goal

Brush your skin gently every other day with a soft bristle brush before you bathe or shower. This unblocks the pores, boosts circulation, and stimulates the lymphatic system. (Wash the brush thoroughly after each use.)

December

Monday	Tuesday	Wednesday

"The weak can never forgive. Forgiveness is the attribute of the strong."
Mahatma Gandhi (1869–1948)

BREAKING THE CHAIN OF BLAME

We often feel tempted to pass on blame to someone else in apparent vindication of ourselves—even though at least some of the fault may lie at our own door. In this way we risk initiating a "chain of blame." It is always more constructive to break the chain, even if it means admitting to more responsibility than we feel in the situation.

Thursday

_____
_____
_____
_____
_____
_____
_____
_____
_____
_____

Friday

_____
_____
_____
_____
_____
_____
_____
_____
_____
_____

Saturday

_____
_____
_____
_____
_____

Sunday

_____
_____
_____
_____
_____

December

Monday	Tuesday	Wednesday

"You are a Sufi when your heart is soft and warm as wool."
Traditional saying

Changing Selves

When experiencing difficulties in a relationship, try switching roles to resolve the issue. Act out a dialogue in which you each take the other's viewpoint, to dramatize your partner's concerns as you imagine them—especially resentments, doubts, and insecurities. Surprising revelations may emerge, pointing the way to a solution.

Thursday

_____
_____
_____
_____
_____
_____
_____
_____
_____
_____
_____
_____

Friday

_____
_____
_____
_____
_____
_____
_____
_____
_____
_____
_____
_____

Saturday

_____
_____
_____
_____
_____

Sunday

_____
_____
_____
_____
_____
_____
_____

December

Monday

Tuesday

Wednesday

"*Reality is a stairway going neither down nor up. We do not move. Today is today, always is today.*"

Octavio Paz (1914–98)

A MEDITATION ON TIME

Time, it is said, is nature's way of preventing everything from happening at once. Meditating on time can help us free ourselves from the tyranny of the clock. If we cling to experiences, we destroy them. The way to wholeness is to kiss each moment as it flies. Reflect on the nature of time without trying to resolve the mystery.

Thursday

Friday

Saturday

Sunday

December

Monday

Tuesday

Wednesday

"The best preacher is the heart; the best teacher is time; the best book is the world; the best friend is God."

Hebrew proverb

HAND AND FOOT

Acupressure at the center of your right palm and just below the ball of each foot will calm the mind and emotions. Ask someone else to exert gentle pressure on these points as you lie comfortably. This will facilitate the flow of chi to your mind, send energy through your body, and leave you in a peaceful state of relaxation.

Thursday

_____
_____
_____
_____
_____
_____
_____
_____
_____
_____
_____
_____
_____

Friday

_____
_____
_____
_____
_____
_____
_____
_____
_____
_____
_____
_____
_____

Saturday

_____
_____
_____
_____
_____
_____

Sunday

_____
_____
_____
_____
_____
_____

December

Monday	Tuesday	Wednesday

"I am you, O God. ... Your soul and my soul resemble two lamps, together shedding one light."
al-Hallaj (*c.*858–922 CE)

THE LIFE OF THE FLAME

A candle consumes its wick, yet we do not value the flame any less for being exhaustible. Think of life as a positive and miraculous illumination, as you gaze into a candle flame and watch its flickering. However wayward the movement of the flame, there is also something enduring about it—like the divine light at the center of every human being.

Thursday

_____
_____
_____
_____
_____
_____
_____
_____
_____
_____
_____
_____
_____

Friday

_____
_____
_____
_____
_____
_____
_____
_____
_____
_____
_____
_____
_____

Saturday

_____
_____
_____
_____
_____
_____

Sunday

_____
_____
_____
_____
_____
_____

Published in 2001 by
Duncan Baird Publishers
Sixth Floor
Castle House
75-76 Wells Street
London, W1T 3QH

Created by Duncan Baird Publishers
Designed by Duncan Baird Publishers

Acknowledgments
The Publishers would like to thank the following for help with translations from foreign texts:
Jane Crediton, Esther de Souza, Dr. Carl Maraspini, Susan Renshaw, Dr. Benedict Stolling,
Rainer Wagner. Copyright on these translations resides with the translators. Grateful thanks
are given for permission to reproduce further copyright material: Martin Luther King, Jr. (from
Strength to Love, Harper Collins, 1963); Alice Walker (from *The Color Purple*, Harcourt Brace
Jovanovich, 1982); Yogaswami (from *Positive Thoughts for Daily Meditation*, Element, 1993);
excerpt from *Present Moment Wonderful Moment: Mindfulness Verses for Daily Living*, 1990 by
Thich Nat Hanh with permission of Parallax Press, Berkeley, California.

Illustrations by Sarah Ball, Claire Bushe, and Katarzyna Klein
Cover illustration by Paul Zwolak
Line artwork by Chris Lee Jones

British Library Cataloguing-in-Publication Data:
A CIP record for this book is available from the British Library.

ISBN: 1-903296-41-2

10 9 8 7 6 5 4 3 2 1

Typeset in Bernhard Modern
Colour reproduction by Colourscan, Singapore
Printed and bound in China by Imago

Note
The abbreviations CE and BCE
are used throughout this book:
BCE: Before Common Era (equivalent of BC)
CE: Common Era (equivalent of AD)